How to
Skim
a Stone

Ralph Jones is a freelance writer, journalist and comedy performer. His writing has appeared in the *New Yorker*, the *Guardian*, *GQ*, *Vice* and the *New Statesman*, and he has been shortlisted for the Anthony Burgess Prize, a BSME Rising Star Award and a PPA Award. He is a performer and head writer for the sketch group The Awkward Silence, and he produces Criminal, a murder mystery improv night and podcast, which has starred comedians including Miles Jupp, Deborah Frances-White, and Rachel Parris. *How to Skim a Stone* is his first book.

Little Ways
to live a
Big Life

How to
Skim
a Stone

Ralph Jones

Quercus

First published in Great Britain in 2020 by

Quercus Editions Ltd
Carmelite House
50 Victoria Embankment
London EC4Y 0DZ
An Hachette UK company

A CIP catalogue record for this book is available from the British Library.

ISBN 978 1 52941 049 5
Ebook ISBN 978 1 52941 048 8

Every effort has been made to contact copyright holders.
However, the publishers will be glad to rectify in future editions
any inadvertent omissions brought to their attention.

10 9 8 7 6 5 4 3 2 1

Text designed and typeset by CC Book Production
Illustrations by Vyvyan Almond
Author photo taken by Natasha Pszenicki
Printed and bound in Great Britain by Clays Ltd, Elcograf S.p.A.

Contents

CHAPTER 1

Why we love to skim

Stone skimming is one of the most contagious activities that human beings have ever devised. Seeing someone skimming a stone nearby and not joining in is like being given a party popper and not pulling the string.

To stand next to a lake and send a stone skimming across the water's surface is to feel thrillingly part of something greater: some almost supernatural trick, some secret triumph over nature's laws. When else do we see rocks dance and skate and fly like birds? Done well, stone skimming looks every bit like a miracle, as though the stone is walking on water, made of something far lighter than mere rock.

In Japan they call stone skimming *mizukiri*, which means 'water cutting'. After it's released from the hand, the stone does indeed appear to be slicing across the water – almost like a letter opener through paper. The array of affectionate terms for the sport across the world is testament to how vividly it captures the imagination. In various languages it is likened to the motion of a frog: it is 'frog jumps' (*bengbaji*) in Bengali and 'letting the frogs out' (*zapuskaty zhabky*) in Ukrainian. In Catalan it is the adorable 'making stepstone bridges' (*fer passeres*); when you skim in Mongolia you are 'making the dog lick' (*nokhoi doloolgokh*); and in Poland you are 'letting the ducks out' (*puszczanie kaczek*).

Welshman Ron Long, a champion stone skimmer aged seventy-five, has been skimming since he was a boy. In 1992, when he was a firefighter, he was seriously injured after a hotel roof fell on him. Fifteen years later, aged sixty-four, he was in Corfu when he rediscovered the pastime. It became a way of rebuilding his atrophied upper-body muscles. Stone skimming was Long's reprieve and he is therefore better placed than almost anyone to comment on the allure of the sport. 'We are conditioned to understand that a stone thrown into water sinks,' he tells me over a pub lunch, saying 'Yeah?' between each sentence. 'And it doesn't. It dances. It skips. It smiles. It laughs. And that's good for the soul. It's anarchic, in a way – you are defying convention and realities.'

This is a common sentiment among stone skimmers. A good skim looks as though it has contradicted the laws of gravity. The stone has no *right* to behave that way. There may be a thrill to be had in watching someone throw a javelin or a discus but the way in which a skimmed stone interacts with water is unique and gloriously peculiar. For a moment, and in a delightful way, the world doesn't look exactly as it should. 'It's very much like fairies dancing on the water,' says Christina Bowen Bravery, who won the women's category in the 2019 World Stone Skimming Championships. 'It is a magical feeling.' If ever you are lucky enough to skim on ice, you might hear that with each bounce the stone makes a wonderful noise akin to the chirruping of a bird. 'I often compare a skimming stone to seeing fireworks, or a shooting star, or a rainbow, or a good magician,' says Kurt Steiner, an American champion skimmer with a wild grey beard and sparkly eyes. 'There are certain observations that just confound the brain and put it in an archaic, awe-struck mode.'

Most of us will remember skimming as a child on some vacation or other, perhaps in the shaded quiet of a river or in the salty face of a seaside wind. This is why the sport (if it has championships, we can call it a sport) appeals to so many of us. It is unusual enough to be memorable, but common enough that we all have memories of having done it in our youth. As someone with good hand-eye coordination, I have always loved stone skimming and been something of a bounce addict, jogging down to the beach whenever family holidays gave me the chance, and collecting as many stones as my hands could cope with. When I watched the Richard Curtis film *About Time* recently on a flight, I felt tears well up in my eyes as the main character and his father (Domhnall Gleeson and Bill Nighy) travelled back in time to when they had skimmed stones together on the beach, care-free, splashing in the sea. Curtis will have chosen skimming because little better illustrates the blissful absence of responsibility that washes over us when we are a child on holiday. Perhaps this is what makes the sport so enchanting. Stone skimming is a time machine.

And, of course, the beauty of stone skimming is that it requires only two things: a stone and some water. Hunting for the perfect stone is a thrill: scrabbling among the pebbles to find a sufficiently flat specimen; the tentative steps towards competence: the splashes, the sploshes, the howling errors, the gradual improvement; and then that one skim – did you see that?? – the one that flew for hours and hours, as if guided onwards by some divine hand, sinking only at the last, too exhausted to resist the water's heavy pull.

In a world that has become suffused with screens, skimming a stone is a haven. Like other activities it would be uncouth to mention here, it is one of the few truly satisfying experiences in life that can be enjoyed free of charge. The practice forces you outside. It is impossible to skim a stone without venturing into an expanse of open air; like golf, it is not a hobby that lends itself to being practised at home, or even in a local sports centre. 'There's a primality involved in any throwing activity,' says Ron Long. 'Man survived by his ability to throw. Deep down in your DNA there's a throwing gene.'

But for all its contemplative qualities, stone skimming has another side. A competitive side. An addictive side. It is a sport with Guinness World Records: Dougie Isaacs, a flint-eyed Scot who puts

down his cigarette only to pick up a stone, can skim farther than any other person on earth: 121.8 metres. Kurt Steiner holds the record for the highest number of bounces for stone 'skipping' (the term they favour in the US): he once skimmed a stone with eighty-eight bounces.

When world records are possible, passions run high and reputations are at stake. In the last decade therefore, and perhaps as the sport has been more widely filmed and broadcast, stone skimming has become something of a battleground. People's infatuation with the sport can see them fly across the world, be interviewed by glossy magazines, and, in one case, spend thousands of pounds in pursuit of the perfect equipment. An entire film, *Skips Stones for Fudge*, was made about the rivalry between Kurt Steiner and former world record holder Russ Byars. This is the element that had me hooked. To me there is something irresistibly fascinating about people taking something so innocent so seriously.

As yet there is no money in the sport – contestants

spend money, they don't make it – but is it conceivable that stone skimming will gather enough momentum to one day become an Olympic sport? Stranger things have happened. As you will learn, the practice takes a significant amount of physical skill. Perhaps it should join dressage and skateboarding as a sport for which you could one day be rewarded with a gold medal. Perhaps stone skimming's day has come.

In this book I aim to teach you how to become a better stone skimmer and to appreciate the beauty and skill inherent in a hobby you may have taken for granted. You will be introduced to people who take stone skimming very seriously indeed, and people who will explain the science of how human hands can make ordinary objects do such beautiful things. You may not set a new Guinness World Record (although who knows?) but, by the end of the book, you should at the very least have improved – perhaps a little, perhaps immeasurably.

By the time you finish the last page, I hope to have

made sure that you never look at stone skimming the same way again. I want you to take this book and run with it under your arm to your nearest body of water – run to a lake, run to the coast, run to an unusually large pond – and I want you to skim stones.

To do that, you're going to need to understand how it works.

CHAPTER 2

The basics

You may not know it but you already understand the basics of how to skim a stone. How? Think for a moment about swimming, not skimming. You already know that if you're on the edge of a swimming pool and want to travel forward into the water, your worst option is to simply collapse onto the surface of the pool in a spectacular belly flop. You know that what you want to do instead is alter the angle of your body and streamline yourself: leaping from the side, you want to travel as close to parallel with the surface of the water as possible with as much force as you can reasonably generate. This isn't skimming but it's not far off: you have already understood that a body won't travel forward on water if it hasn't got either sufficient horizontal velocity or a shallow enough 'angle of attack'.

And, when you go hunting for stones on a beach or the edge of a lake, you understand enough about physics to appreciate the basics of what a good skimming stone looks like. When it comes to skimming, choosing the right stone is crucial. If you found a stone that was ball-shaped and weighed nine kilos, you'd know intuitively that it was a rubbish contender for the job in hand. One of the skills of a champion stone skimmer – one that has been earned over countless hours of trial and error – is meticulously selecting stones that already give the thrower a good chance of success. When I visit Ron Long at his home in Welshpool he says, 'Doesn't matter how good Ronnie O'Sullivan is on the snooker table – give him a banana as the cue and oranges and lemons as the balls, and he's crap.'

Finding the perfect stone for you can be like a jockey finding the horse to which they are perfectly suited: one stone may work very well in your hands, and less well in someone else's. Ron Long likes to use a square stone. Alex Lewis, an intense, athletic twenty-four-year-old Scot who carries a business card on which he describes himself as an 'international stone skimmer', favours stones heavier than those chosen by his rivals. It is not uncommon to see Kurt Steiner skimming with a stone that takes up almost the entirety of his outstretched hand. Through trial and error you will find the kind that's best for you – to some extent this will depend on how much power you have, how tall you are, and the size of your hand. There is far more complex maths at play, which we'll explore in the next chapter.

To be good at stone skimming you must try to master timing and power. In this respect the sport has parallels with a host of others – golf, discus and tennis, to name three. Alex Lewis, who has won several championships including the Welsh, British and All England, used to be a prodigious javelin thrower. If you're good at one, you're likely to be good at the other. If you've found that people have made admiring noises at your handling of a frisbee, I would advise that you run off to your nearest lake and get skimming.

Pick up your stone. Feel it in your hand. Too light or thin and the wind will rob it of its power – or, as Ron Long says, 'I can throw a walnut further than a ping-pong ball.' Too heavy, however, and the stone won't sail, it will plop. If the stone has a flatter side, says Kurt Steiner, make sure it is facing downwards. The stone rests in between your index finger and your thumb, these two digits forming something of a claw, with the three others bent into your palm alongside one another. 'Curl your finger around the stone,' says Christina Bowen Bravery. 'If it has a little edge for your finger to hook into, great.' When it comes to generating all-important spin – 'No spin, no skim,' as champion skimmer Paul Crabtree says – it will be your index finger doing the work. 'In addition to training the muscles that do the projection you need to train the finger that does the spinning,' says Ron Long. 'There are many methods by which you might train this index finger. I'll leave most of it to your imagination.'

There are as many skimming techniques as there are skimmers. Let's assume you're right-handed. A good start is to stand with your body parallel-left to the water – as a golfer would stand parallel-left to the hole – with your legs slightly further apart than your hips. Kurt Steiner advises fixing your eyes not on where you want the stone to land initially but somewhere on the horizon, where you want it to end its journey.

Begin your movement by transferring weight over to your left. When I skim stones on a pond with Alex Lewis on a beautiful March morning in Edinburgh, I watch his technique. He compares his motion to an infinity symbol: he starts by bringing his arm diagonally up across his body and over his head, and then, as he is bending down slightly, his arm crosses back and

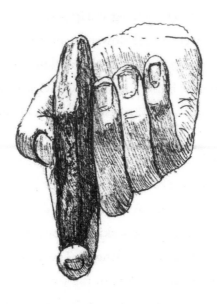

extends behind him. At the top of his backswing, his arms are at about five to three. As though wielding a slingshot, he then brings his arm forward, transferring his energy onto his left leg and imparting spin into the stone. If it were a little slower the process would look much like a wizard theatrically wielding a wand. Do that motion at home and you'll see what I mean. In a tournament Lewis's farthest throw is 111 metres but he believes he has skimmed over 130 metres in private. (I've skimmed about 10 kilometres in private.)

There are two aims in the world of stone skimming: distance or number of skips. As children, we tend to want to achieve as many skips as possible, but tournaments tend to reward length. There is generally a positive correlation between the two. But, whatever your aim, the techniques don't differ significantly. What you're trying to do is throw the stone so that it lands on the water close to flat. As it leaves your hand it will begin to turn over, succumbing to gravity – this is all the more true if the stone is not perfectly symmetrical (which it never is). You can't stop it from turning over, Ron Long explains, but what you need to do is hold it so that when it leaves your hand it's tilted ever so slightly upwards – by the time it reaches the water it will therefore have levelled out. This is all the more true if you are aiming for it not to touch the water until it has been in the air for some time. We will discuss the much-contested angles of the sport in the next chapter.

Remember: it isn't just your fingers and hand doing the work. The world's best skimmers generate an impressive amount of power when they release the stone. 'You're throwing it with your whole body as invested in the palm of your hand,' says Ron Long. Kurt Steiner embodies this teaching, lifting his left leg in the air as he raises the stone above his head, and following through with such force (he throws at around 80 km/h) that his right foot stamps down on the ground, the rest of his body often unable to stop itself being propelled onwards.

Steiner tries to skim the stone so that after it's hit the water, its exit trajectory is as flat as possible. If you watch a skim in which the opposite takes place – in other words, the stone hits the water and rises at a steep angle like 45 degrees, for example – you will see that the stone is liable to spin out of control, losing valuable distance as it rises up or sprays sideways.

If you put these techniques into effect, you should see a marked improvement. The sensation of watching a stone behave in the way you intended is an addictive one. You will find that you know you've hit the sweet spot as soon as the stone touches the water. What you're aiming for is that this first contact is so light, so glancing, that it makes no noise whatever. Then, as your stone sails into the distance, seemingly of its own accord, a beautiful warm feeling will come over you. 'If it had a soul,' says Ron Long, 'the stone's soul would be singing.'

You'll then find yourself scrabbling around for more stones, thinking that you've finally nailed the technique once and for all. A good deal more trial and error will lie ahead of you. But treasure your good throws – it is not easy to skim a stone well. 'It's all just a happily intractable susceptibility of natural biology,' says Kurt Steiner. He means it's a lot of fun. But, in the next chapter, things are going to get less fun and a lot more serious. Strap in.

CHAPTER 3

How to become a skim master

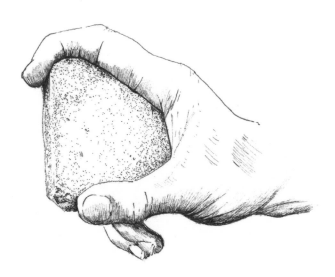

In this chapter we're going to take things up a notch.

In order to become adept at something, it helps to understand the mechanics of what's involved. After you have grasped the concept, it is hard to be worse at the activity than you were to begin with. Obviously there are limits to the application of this theory – Albert Einstein could have explained the aerodynamics of a moving football but he never played up front for Bayern Munich – but appreciating the physics behind stone skimming will stand you in good stead if you want to become a true master (or a fantastic tosser, to use the correct terminology).

Skimming looks almost like witchcraft. It is not, of course. It would be convenient if the laws of nature were suspended every time a stone was skimmed but science can explain the pastime pretty comprehensively, all the while making it more beautiful – if a little more complex.

On a blustery day in March I cycle over to meet Professor John Ockendon in his office at the University of Oxford's Mathematical Institute. In the 1980s representatives from the shipbuilding industry approached Ockendon, an applied mathematician of great renown. They wanted the charismatic expert to investigate something. In rough seas, a ship's keel can sustain damage when crashing into the water. What, the shipbuilders wondered, was the maximum pressure the keel could sustain without incurring damage? The pressure that occurs when the keel meets a wave propels the ship upwards. When a spinning stone meets the surface of the water, it is the same hydrodynamic pressure that causes it to skim. 'The initial thump gives it a terrific upward force,' says Ockendon, bouncing out of his chair to draw in red pen on his whiteboard.

Adjudicating on the optimal shape for the stone, Ockendon recommends something axially symmetric; in other words, something whose appearance is unchanged if rotated around an axis. 'Whenever it bounces you want it to be doing some sort of optimal bounce,' he says. 'Only when it's circularly symmetric will it always be doing the optimal bounce.'

Ockendon is far from the only academic to bring his intellect to bear on the problem of stone skimming. Another of the mathematicians to whom the problem has appealed is Frank Smith of University College London, who was once one of Ockendon's students. In a Skype call with me, Smith, who is sweet and soft-spoken, agrees about the shape, saying that the ideal stone would be something like a tiny flying saucer: a relatively thick, axially symmetric disc with a very shallow dome on either side. In terms of specific thickness, Kurt Steiner – who has probably skimmed hundreds of thousands of stones – prescribes a thickness of about 8 millimetres.

As Steiner points out, stones with all the above traits are of course fiendishly difficult to find in the wild – the reason some skimming champions can be a little dismissive of the academics who prescribe how best to skim. Steiner also points out that it can be helpful to have a little nook in the stone, into which you hook your spin finger. He says that if you want to skim it more than 100 metres, there is a minimum weight you want your stone to be. His stones are between 140 and 200 grams. The densest material available is ideal: 'This permits reduced stone thickness without losing rotational and forward stability, which in turn reduces air drag.' Slate has these characteristics, as does shale, which Steiner finds by Lake Erie, a few hours from his home in Pennsylvania. Granite shares these traits but, again, it's not easy to come across.

Frank Smith, who has written several academic papers about stone skimming, became interested in 2001 when the aerospace industry asked him to work on the problem of 'icing' in aircraft. When a plane flies through clouds in freezing temperatures, ice crystals move over the aircraft's leading edge, and, while some bounce off and others melt, what is also observable is that a form of skimming takes place. 'If the particles come in vertically, at a small angle, then they can skim,' Smith says. This is one of the various ways that understanding skimming can help us solve real-world problems (and vice versa).

A great deal of the heated discussion about stone skimming revolves around the all-important angles involved. One is the tilt, or the angle of attack. This is the angle at which the stone is raised when it leaves your hand. Hold your left hand at a right angle to your body, palm down. Now begin to tilt your fingers upwards slightly. This angle is your hand's angle of attack, assuming it is travelling from left to right.

Because the stone has had spin imparted on it, it will also be kept at this angle – for a while – by something called gyroscopic stabilisation: the same principle that keeps a bicycle upright. The faster the stone rotates, the more stable it will be as it moves through the air (or water). 'Things that are spinning don't like to have their axis of rotation altered,' says John Ockendon.

A layman might suspect – I certainly did – that the optimal skimming angle would simply be as shallow as possible. After all, the stone needs to be gliding across the water. And how do things glide? By travelling parallel across whatever surface they're on. All of the experts, however, say that this is not the case. In 2004, for the journal *Nature*, Christophe Clanet and Lydéric Bocquet fired aluminium discs out of a catapult onto water and, famously, determined that the optimal skimming angle was 20 degrees. So why is it not desirable to throw the stone as horizontally as possible?

One practical issue is that if a person is 1.5 metres above the water and they try to get much lower in order to minimise the angle, a lot of power can be taken out of the throw – given, as we have established, that it involves the entire body. (Picture a tennis player trying to serve while crouching and you get the idea.) But the more scientific answer concerns the way that the stone reacts when it makes contact with the water.

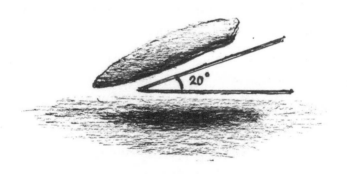

Professor Tadd Truscott is a fluid dynamicist at the department of mechanical and aerospace engineering at Utah State University. Truscott, who is wavy-haired and wonderfully buoyant himself, heads a team called Splash Lab, which, among other things, examines how objects skim on water. 'The rock wants to go into the water but the water is dense enough that it's creating enough lift for it to pop back up,' he explains. 'But as you go to, say, 5 degrees, that might not be true any more – your lift is very small.' So, says Truscott, your low angle may struggle to keep the stone aloft for long because, just as a wave propels a boat upwards, the water is constantly helping to keep the stone afloat. 'You want it to fly,' says John Ockendon, 'so you've got to get a decent upwards force on each bounce.'

Here's why that matters. Water is 1,000 per cent denser than air and so the stone will travel considerably faster through air than water. A shallower angle, says Truscott, means that the stone will make a more pro-longed initial impact with the water, thereby slowing it down more than if this initial impact had only been glancing – in other words, if the angle had been a little steeper. Truscott agrees with Clanet, having discovered in experiments that the optimal angle is between 18 and 20 degrees.

It is important to note, however, what Clanet was focusing on: number of skims. Ron Long, who is not alone in prioritising distance over quantity, dismisses 20 degrees as silly. When I skim with him in his garden in Welshpool ('It would be quicker to train a monkey,' he says of me), he tells me that the optimal angle is in fact 5 degrees. At 20 degrees, he says, 'You're confronting the water, you're slapping into it.' You should aim, he says, for the stone to kiss the water. In order to achieve 5 degrees, however, Long performs a throw in which the stone travels a significant distance before making contact with the water. This makes sense, of course – the longer the distance travelled by the stone, the shallower the angle at impact.

Long has certainly given the problem a lot of thought. He shows me into his house and turns on his computer. There he shows me the drawings he has made to illustrate how someone ought to skim a stone. Assuming the average man is 1.7 metres tall and the average woman 1.6 metres tall, Long's illustrations show that in order to achieve his 5-degree angle, the stone's initial contact with the water would need to happen around 15 metres from your hand. This specific aspect of the sport – where to land your first skim – is not well studied. Steiner says that when he is skimming he might look for an initial contact at about 6–10 metres and when he is skipping he would aim for 2–4 metres. Keisuke Hashimoto, a stocky Japanese man who took the skimming world by surprise when he won the world championships with an elegant technique in 2017, tells me over Twitter that he releases the stone at knee height. He aims to contact the water early because he feels the longer the stone is in the air, the more unpredictable it becomes. If he were aiming only for distance, he says, his first skim might contact the water later. 'But I want to skim beautiful.'

When Truscott and his team experimented with

skimming a polyurethane ball, they managed to skim it 150 metres. (They discovered that when an elastic ball hits the water, for a few hundredths of a second it deforms into the shape of a disc, doubling its surface area.) What they observed was that it didn't skip all that many times. Truscott thinks that if you want to skim a stone as far as possible, you ought to focus simply on increasing the power you generate. Do this, at a relatively shallow angle, and the gaps between the skips ought to be greater, generating fewer overall skips as a result and therefore – crucially – being slowed down by water as little as possible.

The other angle to mention is the exit angle, the angle at which the stone leaves the water. This angle will be determined by the angle of attack (a shallow angle of attack should give you a shallow exit angle) and the science tells us that you want the two to be around the same: between 18 and 20 degrees. Kurt Steiner thinks backwards and aims for the stone's exit angle to be between 5 and 10 degrees. This will mean that this is roughly the angle at which his stone enters the water.

It is essential to point out that science does not have all the answers. In a 2002 paper in the *American Journal of Physics* entitled 'The physics of stone skipping', Lydéric Bocquet seemed to estimate the maximum possible number of skips as thirty-eight – the world record at the time. Eleven years later, Kurt Steiner more than doubled this number with eighty-eight. Tadd Truscott says that even eighty-eight will start to look easy once the world of stone skimming starts attracting major-league baseball pitchers, who can throw up to 160 km/h. When this happens, he says, someone might skip a stone more than 300 times.

So if you want to skim like a pro, look for a flying saucer-shaped stone, 8 millimetres thick, weighing about 170 grams, with a little nook for your index finger. Throw it with as much force as you can generate. If distance is your ambition, try to strike the water at around 10 metres from your hand, at an angle of about 10 degrees. If you are aiming for as many skips as possible, try to strike the water earlier, at around 7.5 metres, at an angle of about 19 degrees. Watch as your stone dances and disappears into the distance.

Done that? Good. Now it's time to enter some competitions.

CHAPTER 4

Competitions

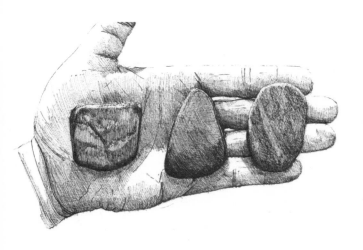

The World Stone Skimming Championships take place on the tiny Scottish island of Easdale, home to only sixty people and formerly the home of the Scottish slate industry. There, every September, hundreds of budding skimmers show up and skim slate in a flooded quarry. They each have three throws. The stone, which must be three inches in diameter or less, has to touch the water at least three times and stay within the buoys that form a lane all the way up to the back wall, 63 metres away. Anyone who strikes the back wall — as determined by a line of judges in fancy dress, who watch from the surrounding cliffs – qualifies for the final, where the best cumulative score from three throws wins the title. (There is also a prize for the best older skimmer – 'Old Tosser' – which Ron Long has tended to win.) It looks relatively easy, but when I took part in 2019, one of my skims travelled 43 metres and the other two went out of bounds. Please stop laughing.

Easdale's is the original and the most famous skimming tournament but it's far from the only one. Stone skimming has gone global. As well as the championships in Britain – there is the British, the All England Open, and the Welsh Open – there are tournaments in the Netherlands, the US, Switzerland and Japan, at the very least.

Unlike sports whose championships have existed for far longer, like football or tennis, stone skimming tournaments have idiosyncrasies. Most of them simply reward length – I am not aware of a championship that prizes number of skips above everything else

– but there are exceptions. Four-time champion Kei-suke Hashimoto tells me that in Japan there are three competitions: the Hokkaido tournament in July; the international championship in Kochi in August; and, in October, the All-Japan tournament in Miyagi. 'We have unique rules,' he says about the international championship. 'Evaluation points include not only distance and count of skips, but also beauty ripples and trajectories.' In this sense, Japan treats skimming a little like gymnastics or diving, where technical and aesthetic qualities are rewarded. It doesn't necessarily matter that you skimmed it further than your opponent; did you skim beautifully?

In the final of the tournament in Kochi, the two remaining contenders wear a red or a blue sash. After each has skimmed, the judges raise a flag corresponding to the colour of the sash they believed threw better, according to their criteria. On the one hand the criteria eliminate an element of the controversy that can bedevil any skimming tournament – it is difficult to objectively ascertain distance simply by eye – but on the other, the judgment becomes all the more subjective.

This brings us to the subject of standardisation, about which Ron Long feels passionately. Long regularly compares skimming to an Olympic sport, where everyone uses standardised equipment. He thinks little of tournaments where contestants choose their own stones and has thought for a long time that the stones used in championships ought to be standardised, to level the playing field. 'If you were practising with a particular stone of a particular weight and you know it's exactly the same weight all the time,' he says, 'you can condition your musculature to maximise the power that you put into it.' As he says on his website, 'If stone skimming is to gain acceptance outside of its devotees and be considered a "proper" sport worthy of consideration and promotion, then it is essential that it have consistent rules and equipment.'

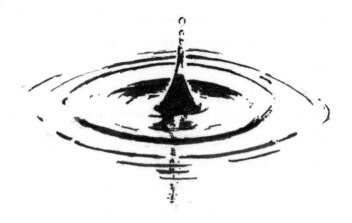

Long set about designing standardised stones. At his home in Welshpool he shows me hundreds of them, and we skim them in his garden, where he also constructed a pond and a wooden skimming platform in the spring of 2019 at a cost of around £4,000. The stones, on which Long used a brooch to brand the image of a dragon, are Scottish hardstone grit and were made by a decorative stone manufacturer living in nearby Caersws. They are gorgeous. There is a triangular, a square, and a circular model. There are four categories (50g, 80g, 110g, and 140g) but, within each category, every stone is identical in weight and surface area. Long buys them from the manufacturer for 49 pence each and then sells them to competition organisers for the same price. (You can buy them from his website: ronlongoldtosser.eu.) The Welsh and the Swiss championships use his standardised stones, and he believes that there are plenty of people who would like to run competitions but lack the necessary stones. They could use his, he says.

Alex Lewis has thought about the possibility of creating an indoor world championship, in which the water is 0.3 metres deep and 140 metres long. It would make sense in this context to have standardised stones, he thinks. But he says that standardisation might take the fun out of combing a beach in search of stones to skim – one of the joys of the sport. It's easy to see his point. What is happening, essentially, is that as the sport becomes more popular, the gulf is widening between those who wander down to tournaments on a sunny day for a laugh and those who want the sport to be taken seriously because they are incredibly good at it. Lewis tells me that world record holder Dougie Isaacs has spoken about initiating a masters tournament, only open to people who have skimmed more than 85 metres in the past.

Both Lewis and Long have said in the past that the world championships should not be held in Easdale, given that the maximum distance possible is 63 metres. Long thinks they need to move 'somewhere worthy of the appellation'. He thinks that the Welsh Open, which he helped establish, is the perfect example: contestants can stand on a built-in jetty and skim more than 150 metres in a man-made lake. It has 'all of the elements necessary for the best performances to take place,' he says. I ask Donald Melville, who organises the world championships, whether he admires those who take the sport so seriously. 'Nah, nah,' says Melville, a jovial, patient character. 'It's a family event. It actually starts to belittle the fun behind it if you have too many people taking it too seriously.'

Long thinks that the lengthy process of having his standardised stones made must have cost him at least £4,000. Add to this the pond construction and the numerous trips he has taken to tournaments across the country, and the costs stack up. Some might find this incomprehensible, but Long does not see it this way. 'When I consider the frivolity of people's normal expenditure: ten pints of beer on a Saturday night or a holiday in Torremolinos . . . at least at the end of a stone skimming competition, if you're fortunate you come away with a prize medal around your neck.' With the pond he has made something durable, something that will see years of happy use. 'Should I live to be 155 I shall probably get my money back,' he tells me as he holds a cup of coffee in his kitchen. 'But if all we ever did in life was spend money that we can get back in some way, it would be a very slim existence.'

Pursuing money is obviously not a motivation for the countless people who skim stones across the world. You are unlikely to see a skimming champion sipping Moët and reclining in the back of a Rolls-Royce any time soon. Like the contention that graffiti is perhaps the purest art form because it is done for neither critical acclaim nor financial reward, it could be argued that stone skimming is one of the purest sports. Really, it is our attempt to conquer nature, to feel for a moment that we have made magic happen. Even when there is no one else around, says Ron Long, stone skimming is competitive. We glimpse what is possible and are forever chasing that high.

The Olympics could be one of the possibilities in stone skimming's future. For now, however, it has its devotees and its casual practitioners; it has its moments in the spotlight and it exists in the snapshots our minds remember from summer holidays long ago. Whether you are a girl of seven or a man of seventy-five, you can pick up a stone and throw it with all your might. Stone skimming has been with us forever, and it isn't going anywhere any time soon.

Now get out there and skim some stones.